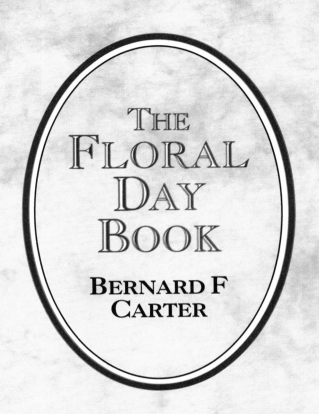

THE FLORAL DAY BOOK

BERNARD F CARTER

Bloomsbury Books
London

The illustrations
in this book have been
selected from
Bernard Carter's
The Floral Birthday Book
published by
Webb & Bower (Publishers) Ltd.
in 1990

Illustration copyright © 1990 Bernard Carter

This edition published exclusively by Bloomsbury Books
an imprint of The Godfrey Cave Group
42 Bloomsbury Street
London
WC1B 3QJ

ISBN 1-85471 445 7
This Edition © 1994 Godfrey Cave

Printed and bound in Great Britain by
BPC Paulton Books Ltd
Member of the British Printing Company Ltd.
10 9 8 7 6 5 4 3 2 1

JANUARY

Snowdrops

Grass – **UTILITY**

Bay – **GLORY**

Ivy – **FRIENDSHIP**

Laurel – **AMBITION**

JANUARY

1

2

3

4

5

6

7

8

Cypress – **MOURNING**

Box – **FIRMNESS**

Ice Plant – **REJECTED ADDRESSES**

Arbutus – **LOVE OR FRIENDSHIP**

Turnip – CHARITY

Heath – SOLITUDE

Cresses – STABILITY

9

10

11

12

13

14

15

16

Sage – **DOMESTIC VIRTUES**

Lichen – **DEJECTION**

Fir – **ELEVATION**

Iceland Moss – **HEALTH**

Orange – **GENEROSITY**

Monterey Cypress – **CONSTANT**

Arbor Vitae – **UNCHANGING FRIENDSHIP**

Laurustinus – **'I DIE IF NEGLECTED'**

17

18

19

20

JANUARY

21

22

23

24

Endive – FRUGALITY

Ilex – ENDURANCE

Fennel – STRENGTH

Ground Ivy – HUMILITY

Cineraria – **A STAR**

Thyme – **THRIFTINESS**

Olive – **PEACE**

Stonecrop – **TRANQUILLITY**

JANUARY

25

26

27

28

JANUARY

29

30

31

Truffle – SURPRISE

Variegated Holly – ALWAYS CHEERFUL

White Ivy – RARITY

FEBRUARY

Daffodils

Snowdrops (seed heads)

Camellia

Lesser periwinkle

Lesser celandine

February

1

2

3

4

Corsican Pine – 'YOU BEWILDER ME'

Snowdrop – HOPE

Champignon – SUSPICION

Clematis – POVERTY

FEBRUARY

Crocus – **ABUSE NOT**

Camellia Japonica – **PITY**

Opuntia – **SATIRE**

Almond Tree – **INDISCRETION**

5

6

7

8

FEBRUARY

9

10

11

12

Kalmia – **NATURE**

Primula – **ANIMATION**

Spring Crocus – **YOUTHFUL GLADNESS**

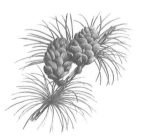

Larch – **DECEITFUL CHARMS**

Tree Poppy – **LOVE'S ORACLE**

Pyrus Japonica – **LOVE AT FIRST SIGHT**

Irish Ivy – **CLINGING AFFECTION**

Purple Violet – **'YOU OCCUPY MY THOUGHTS'**

FEBRUARY

13

14

15

16

February

17

18

19

20

Daffodil – CHIVALRY

Daisy – CHEERFULNESS

Flowering Currant – SELF-REVERENCE

Arum Lily – ARDOUR

Gorse – **ENDURING AFFECTION**

Reeds – **MUSIC**

Variegated Laurel – **ATTRACTIVE**

Escallonia – **'I LIVE FOR THEE'**

FEBRUARY

21

22

23

24

FEBRUARY

25

26

27

28

Cyclamen – **HOPE**

Hepatica – **CONFIDENCE**

Garden Daisy – **'I SHARE YOUR SENTIMENTS'**

Buttercup – **CHILDHOOD**

Bullrush – **DOCILITY**

29

NOTES

MARCH

Three-cornered leek

Narcissus

Blackthorn

Spring crocus

Violet

Primrose

Lesser celandine

MARCH

1

2

3

4

Willow – **FORSAKEN**

Blue Violet – **FAITHFULNESS**

Pink Camellia – **ANTICIPATION**

Wallflower – **FIDELITY**

Garden Anemone – **FORSAKEN**

Hyacinth – **SPORT**

Wild Daisy – **INDECISION**

Ivy Spray – **ASSIDUOUS TO PLEASE**

5

6

7

8

9	

10	

11	

12	

Kingcup – 'I WISH I WAS RICH'

White Violet – MODESTY

Marshmallow – KINDNESS

Cucumber – CRITICISM

Double Daffodil – **REGARD**

Mint – **VIRTUE**

Primrose – **YOUTH**

Mustard – **INDIFFERENCE**

MARCH

13

14

15

16

MARCH

17

18

19

20

Auricula – **PAINTING**

Red Periwinkle – **EARLY FRIENDSHIPS**

Orange Blossom – **CHASTITY**

Blue Hyacinth – **CONSTANCY**

Rhubarb – **ADVICE**

Campanula – **'YOU ARE RICH IN ATTRACTION'**

Orchis – **A BEAUTY**

Wild Violet – **LOVE IN IDLENESS**

21

22

23

24

MARCH

25

26

27

28

Lenten Lily – **RECIPROCAL LOVE**

Double Daisy – **PARTICIPATION**

Peppermint – **CORDIALITY**

White Periwinkle – **PLEASANT RECOLLECTIONS**

Heartsease – **THOUGHTS**

Evening Primrose – **INCONSISTANCY**

Polyanthus – **PRIDE OF RICHES**

29

30

31

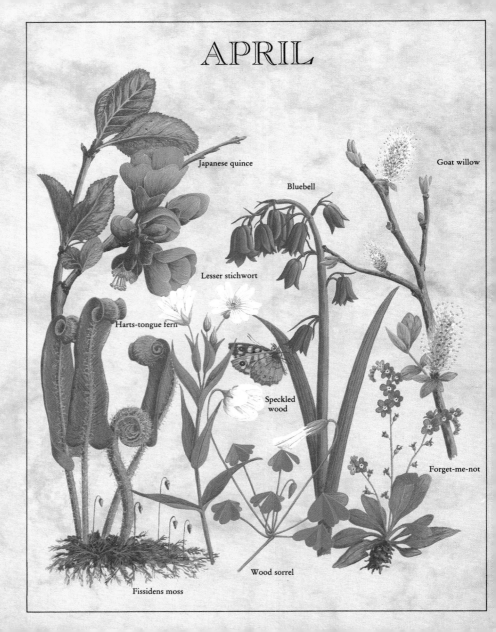

APRIL

Japanese quince

Goat willow

Bluebell

Lesser stichwort

Harts-tongue fern

Speckled wood

Forget-me-not

Wood sorrel

Fissidens moss

APRIL

1

2

3

4

Palm – **VICTORY**

Purple Hyacinth – **SORROW**

Cowslip – **PENSIVENESS**

Wood Anemone – **SICKNESS**

Crimson Polyanthus – **THE HEART'S MYSTERY**

Garden Forget-me-not – **FORGET ME NOT**

Pear Tree – **AFFECTION**

Saffron Meadow – **MIRTH**

APRIL

5

6

7

8

APRIL

9

10

11

12

Lilac Polyanthus – **CONFIDENCE IN HEAVEN**

Globe Ranunculus – **'I AM DAZZLED BY YOUR CHARMS'**

Red Primrose – **UNPATRONISED MERIT**

Peach Blossom – **'I AM YOUR CAPTIVE'**

Apricot Blossom – **DOUBT**

Marjoram – **BLUSHES**

Wild Ranunculus – **INCONSISTANCY**

Cherry Tree – **EDUCATION**

APRIL

13

14

15

16

Injection

Bury

17

18

19

20

Wistaria – REGRET

Sweetbriar – SIMPLICITY

Tendrils of Climbing Plants – LINKS

Blue Periwinkle – PLEASURES OF MEMORY

Wood Sorrel – **JOY**

Red Tulip – **DECLARATION OF LOVE**

Shamrock – **JOY IN SORROW**

Water Willow – **FREEDOM**

21

22

23

24

Injection
Book more
appointments

25

26

27

28

White Cherry Tree – **DECEPTION**

Speedwell – **'YOU ARE MY DIVINITY'**

Larch – **DARING**

Honesty Flowers – **IMMORTALITY**

Filbert Tree – RECONCILIATION

Weeping Willow – MELANCHOLY

29

30

NOTES

MAY

Red campion

Green hairstreak

Wallflower

Hawthorn

Herb
Robert

Sea
campion

Pine

Daisy

Pansy

MAY

1

2

3

4

Forget-me-not – 'FORGET ME NOT'

Saffron – MARRIAGE

Acanthus – THE FINE ARTS

Virginian Creeper – SWEET NEGLECT

Beech Tree – **PROSPERITY**

Celandine – **JOY**

Narcissus – **EGOTISM**

Black Thorn – **DIFFICULTY**

MAY

5

6

7

8

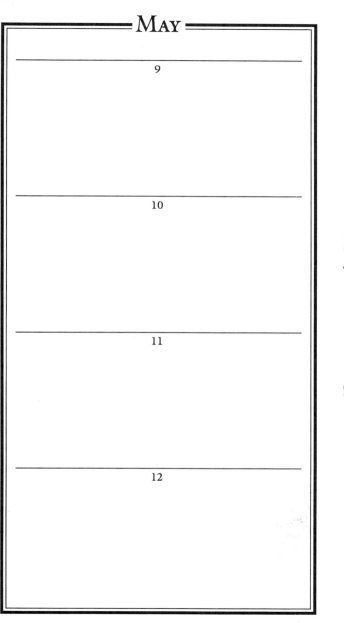

MAY

9

10

11

12

Apple Blossom – CHOICE

Polypody Fern – MEDITATION

Rhododendron – DANGER

Elm – DIGNITY

Lilac – **First Emotions of Love**

Harebell – **Grief**

Chestnut – **Do me Justice**

Water-Lily – **Invocation**

13

14

15

16

MAY

17	
18	
19	
20	

Hawthorn – **HOPE**

Asparagus Fern – **SECRECY**

Syringa – **MEMORY**

Elder – **MERCY**

Osier – CANDOUR

Laburnum – FORSAKEN

Bluebell – CONSTANCY

First Rose of Summer – MAJESTY

MAY

21

22

23

24

MAY

25

26

27

28

Pimpernel – **CHANGE**

Lily of the Valley – **RETURN OF HAPPINESS**

Poplar – **COURAGE**

Red Tulip – **CONFESSION OF LOVE**

MAY

Oak – **HOSPITALITY**

Sothernwood – **MERRIMENT**

Tulip Tree – **FAME**

29

30

Blackpool   31

NOTES

JUNE

Iris

Small heath

Helen Traubel

Boursault (rose)

Hybrid tea (rose)

Rugosa

Great bindweed

JUNE

1

2

3

4

Rose (Gloire de Dijon) – **GLADNESS**

Rose (Apricot) – **'WELCOME ME'**

Rose (Cabbage) – **AMBASSADOR**

Rose (Boursault) – **HAPPY LOVE**

Rose (Austrian) – 'THOU ART ALL THAT IS LOVELY'

Rose (Burgundy) – UNCONSCIOUSNESS

Rose (Unique) – MODESTY

Rose (Caroline) – LOVE IS DANGEROUS

JUNE

5

6

7

8

JUNE

9

10

11

12

Rosebud (White) – **A Heart ignorant of Love**

Rose (Red-leaved) – **Beauty**

Rose (China) – **Grace**

Rose (Rambler) – **'Only deserve my love'**

Rose (Deep Red) – **BASHFULNESS**

Rosebud (Moss) – **CONFESSION OF LOVE**

Rose (Holy) – **PRIDE**

Rose (Moss) – **SUPERIOR MERIT**

13

14

15

16

JUNE

17

18

19

20

Rose (Virginian) – **Compassion**

Rose (Lancaster) – **Union**

Cluster Rose – **'You are charming'**

Rose (Musk) – **A Capricious Beauty**

Rosebud (Red) – **'YOU ARE YOUNG AND BEAUTIFUL'**

Rose (Yellow) – **DEPARTURE OF LOVE**

Rose (York) – **WAR**

Rose (White and Red) – **UNITY**

JUNE

21

Appointment
Chrishine

22

23

24

JUNE

25

26

27

28

Rose (Damask) – **FRESHNESS**

Rose (Mundi) – **VARIETY**

Rose (White) – **'I AM WORTHY OF YOU'**

Rose (Maiden Blush) – **TIMID LOVE**

Rose (White Withered) – **TRANSIENT IMPRESSIONS**

Crown of Roses – **REWARD OF CHASTITY**

29

30

Notes

JULY

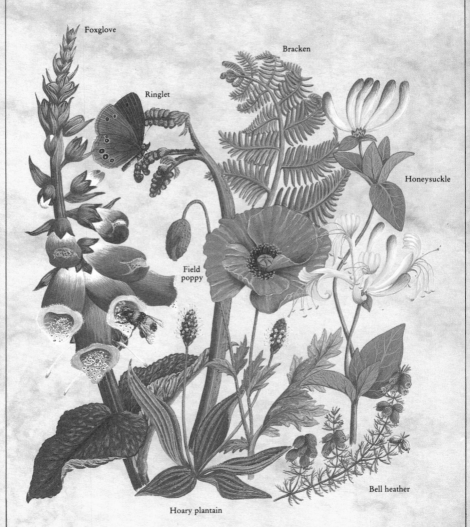

Foxglove

Ringlet

Bracken

Honeysuckle

Field poppy

Bell heather

Hoary plantain

JULY

1

2

3

4

Pink (Carnation) – **BOLDNESS**

White Lily – **PURITY**

Sweet Pea – **DEPARTURE**

Carnation – **WOMAN'S LOVE**

Mignonette – **EXCELLENCE**

Iris – 'I HAVE A MESSAGE FOR YOU'

Imperial Lily – **DIGNITY**

Verbena – **ENCHANTMENT**

5

6

7

8

9

10

11

12

Guelder Rose – **GROWING OLD**

Red Double Pink – **ARDENT LOVE**

Acacia – **CHASTE LOVE**

Striped Carnation – **EXTREMES**

Scarlet Geranium – **COMFORT**

Lotus Flower – **ESTRANGED LOVE**

Day Lily – **COQUETRY**

Lotus – **ELOQUENCE**

JULY

13

14

15

16

JULY

17

18

19

20

Magnolia – **LOVE OF NATURE**

Ivy-leaved Geranium – **GENIUS**

Convolvolus – **EXTINGUISHED HOPE**

Yellow Lily – **EXTREME AMIABILITY**

Yellow Lily – **FALSEHOOD**

Larkspur – **BRIGHTNESS**

Honeysuckle – **RUSTIC BEAUTY**

Balsam – **IMPATIENCE**

JULY

21

22

23

24

25

26

27

28

Yellow Carnation – **DISDAIN**

White Pink – **'YOU ARE FAIR AND FASCINATING'**

Passion Flower – **BELIEF**

Knotweed – **RECANTATION**

JULY

Acacia (Rose) – **PLATONIC LOVE**

Bee Orchis – **INDUSTRY**

Mountain Pink – **AMBITION**

29

30

31

NOTES

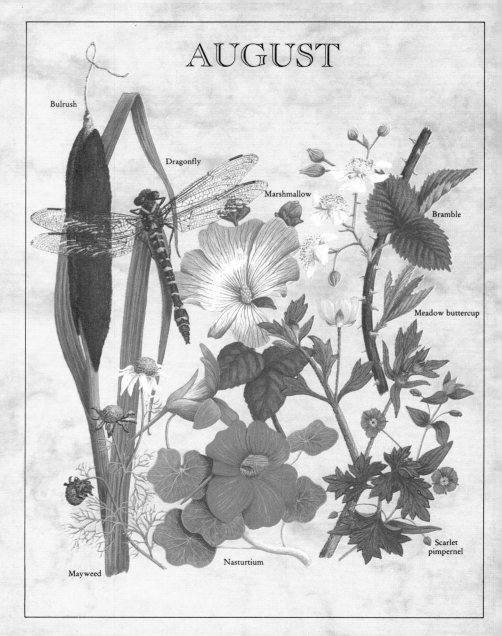

AUGUST

Bulrush

Dragonfly

Marshmallow

Bramble

Meadow buttercup

Scarlet pimpernel

Nasturtium

Mayweed

AUGUST

1

2

3

4

Corn – **RICHES**

Field Red Poppy – **CONSOLATION**

Corn Flower – **PURITY**

Traveller's Joy – **SAFETY**

Oats – **MUSIC**

Wheat – **PROSPERITY**

White Poppy – **SLEEP**

Pink Geranium – **PARTIALITY**

AUGUST

5

6

7

8

9

10

11

12

Crimson Poppy – **FANTASY**

Yellow Jasmine – **GRACE AND ELEGANCE**

Oak-leaved Geranium – 'LADY, DEIGN TO SMILE.'

Broom – **HUMILITY**

Indian Double Pink – **ALWAYS LOVELY**

Peony – **ANGER**

Asphodel – '**MY REGRETS FOLLOW YOU TO THE GRAVE.**'

Coral Honeysuckle – '**THE COLOUR OF MY FATE.**'

AUGUST

13

14

15

16

August

17

18

19

20

Monkshood – **FICKLENESS**

Quaking Grass – **AGITATION**

Snapdragon – **PRESUMPTION**

Stock – **PROMPTITUDE**

Alkanet – **DEVOTION**

Sunflower – **ADORATION**

Banksia – **LOVE SWEET AND SILENT**

Madagasgar Jasmine – **SEPARATION**

21

22

23

24

AUGUST

25

26

27

28

Venus's Looking-glass – **FLATTERY**

Clematis – **MENTAL BEAUTY**

Red Dahlia – **JOY**

Pomegranate – **FOLLY**

August

Borage – **BLUNTNESS**

Camomile – **ENERGY IN ADVERSITY**

Monthly Honeysuckle – **BOND OF LOVE**

29

30

31

NOTES

SEPTEMBER

Bracken

Small heath

Shasta daisy

Tutsan

Tormentil

Bramble

September

1

2

3

4

Apple – **Temptation**

Aloe – **Sorrow**

Geranium (White) – **Refinement**

Mountain Ash – **Intellect**

Aster – **VARIETY**

Berry Wreath – **REWARD**

Nut Tree – **AMUSEMENT**

Nutmeg Geranium – **AN EXPECTED MEETING**

5

6

7

8

9

10

11

12

Double Aster – **RECIPROCITY**

Balm of Gilead – **RELIEF**

Silver-leaved Geranium – **RETROSPECTION**

Birch Tree – **MEEKNESS**

Dew Plant – **A Serenade**

Dahlia – **Elegance and Dignity**

Single Aster – **Indecision**

Daphne – **Ornament**

13

14

15

16

SEPTEMBER

17

18

19

20

Fig – ARGUMENT

Chrysanthemum – CHEERFULNESS

Flax – DOMESTIC VIRTUES

Hop – INJUSTICE

Fuchsia – **TASTE**

Juniper – **PROTECTION**

Hydrangea – **BOASTFULNESS**

Indian Corn – **ECLAT, OR TRIUMPH**

SEPTEMBER

21

22

23

24

25

26

27

28

Lavender – **DISTRUST**

Linden – **CONJUGAL LOVE**

Love-Lies-Bleeding – **HOPELESS**

Maize – **PLENTY**

SEPTEMBER

Michaelmas Daisy – AFTERTHOUGHT

Walnut – STRATAGEM

29

30

OCTOBER

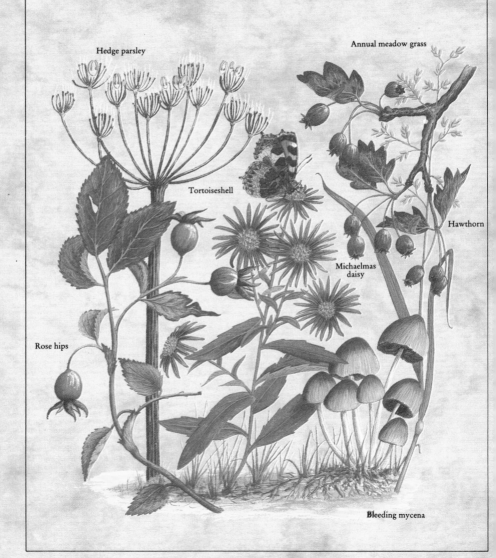

Hedge parsley

Annual meadow grass

Tortoiseshell

Hawthorn

Michaelmas
daisy

Rose hips

Bleeding mycena

OCTOBER

1

2

3

4

Pineapple – **PERFECTION**

Red Chrysanthemum – **LOVE**

Plane Tree – **GENIUS**

Honesty – **FASCINATION**

Pomegranate Blossom – **A WARNING**

Azalea – **ADORATION**

Hollyhock – **FEMALE AMBITION**

Belladonna – **SILENCE**

5

6

7

8

9

10

11

12

Myrtle – **LOVE**

Oak Leaf – **VALOUR**

Nasturtium – **PATRIOTISM**

Black Pine – **PITY**

Wild Plum Tree – **INDEPENDENCE**

Berberis – **AGE**

Everlasting Pea – **'WILT THOU GO WITH ME?'**

Sycamore – **CURIOSITY**

OCTOBER

13

14

15

16

17

18

19

20

Thistle – **AUSTERITY**

Valerian – **ACCOMMODATING DISPOSITION**

Tall Sunflower – **HAUGHTINESS**

Hazel Nuts – **RECONCILIATION**

Vine – **INTOXICATION**

Eucalyptus – **FAREWELL**

Canary Grass – **PERSEVERANCE**

White Chrysanthemum – **TRUTH**

21

22

23

24

OCTOBER

25

26

27

28

Sweet Cicely – **GLADNESS**

Wild Geranium – **STEADFAST PIETY**

Chestnut – **LUXURY**

Purple Columbine – **RESOLUTION**

Dock – PATIENCE

Night-scented Stock – DEVOTION

Yellow Chrysanthemum – SLIGHTED LOVE

29

30

31

NOTES

NOVEMBER

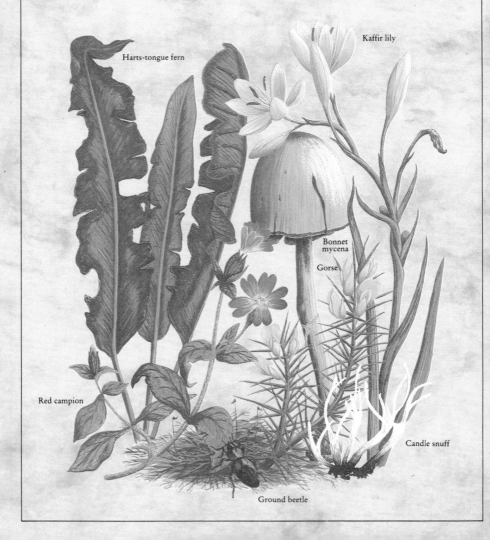

Harts-tongue fern

Kaffir lily

Bonnet
mycena

Gorse

Red campion

Candle snuff

Ground beetle

NOVEMBER

1

2

3

4

Winter Heliotrope – **KINDNESS**

Aspen – **LAMENTATION**

Pitch Pine – **PHILOSOPHY**

Cranberry – **CURE FOR HEARTACHE**

Hemp – **Fate**

Globe Amaranth – **Unchangeable**

Snow Berry – **Thoughts of Heaven**

White Poplar – **Time**

5

6

7

8

9

10

11

12

Ash Tree – **GRANDEUR**

Bay Leaf – **FAITHFULNESS**

Bilberry – **TREACHERY**

Bindweed – **PROFUSENESS**

Cedar of Lebanon – **INCORRUPTIBILITY**

Bramble – **LOWLINESS**

Red Salvia – **POMP**

Variegated Ivy – **BRIGHTNESS**

13

14

15

16

17

18

19

20

Hogweed – **REMEMBRANCE**

Fern Moss – **CONTENT**

Shasta Daisy – **BEAUTY**

Acer – **'YOU ARE HARD'**

Gardinea – **PEACE**

Black Prince Geranium – **DELUSIVE HOPES**

Sorrel – **PARENTAL AFFECTION**

Tufted Vetch – **REASON**

21

22

23

24

NOVEMBER

25

26

27

28

Norway Spruce – **KINDNESS**

Pine Branch – **ASPIRATION**

Variegated Geranium – **CHARMS OF WOMEN**

Helenium – **TEARS**

Czar Violet – **KINDNESS AND WORTH**

Welted Thistle – **MISANTHROPY**

29

30

DECEMBER

Winter heliotrope

Bjerkadera
(fungus)

Polypody fern

Mistletoe

Ivy

Holly

December

1

2

3

4

Monthly Rose – **ENCHANTMENT**

Hyssop – **PURITY**

White Camellia – **EXCELLENCE IN WOMAN**

Scotch Thistle – **RETALIATION**

Withered Leaves – **MELANCHOLY**

Hibiscus – **CHANGE**

Plantain – **OBLIGATION**

Osmunda – **DREAMS**

DECEMBER

5

6

7

8

9

10

11

12

Lemon – **PIQUANCY**

Hibernica – **STRONG FRIENDSHIP**

Bamboo – **HOMAGE**

Broken Straw – **DIVISION**

Hips and Haws – **COMPENSATION**

Wormwood – **ABSENCE**

Winter Heath – **EXILE**

Douglas Fir – **PERSEVERENCE IN PURSUIT OF KNOWLEDGE**

DECEMBER

13

14

15

16

17

18

19

20

Flowering Laurel – **GOODNESS**

Ivy Berry – **WARNING**

Moss – **SECLUSION**

Fern – **SINCERITY**

Broken Stalks – **DISSENSION**

Parsley – **FEASTING**

Trefoil – **REVENGE**

Holly Berries – **GREETINGS**

DECEMBER

21

22

23

24

DECEMBER

25

26

27

28

Mistletoe – 'I SURMOUNT ALL OBSTACLES'

Walnuts – SOCIALITY

Fir Cone – ORDER

Holly – FORETHOUGHT

Helleborus – 'TRANQUILIZE MY ANXIETY'

Ash Twigs – FESTIVITY

Yew – SADNESS

29

30

31